I.S.B.N. 0 85079 152 9

SUNDAY EXPRESS & DAILY EXPRESS CARTOONS

Thirty-ninth Series

AN EXPRESS BOOKS PUBLICATION

Printed in Great Britain by Purnell and Sons (Book Production) Ltd., Paulton, Bristol

£1.95

FOREWORD

by

Sir JOHN JUNOR

Editor of the

Sunday Express

Churchill was in Number Ten Downing Street, Hitler strutted supreme in Europe, General Montgomery was the hero, and Rommel the dreaded enemy when the comic genius of Carl Giles first erupted on the British nation.

All the other actors have long since left the scene.

Churchill in glory. Hitler in flames, Montgomery and Rommel in nostalgia. Eight more Prime Ministers have kissed the Sovereign's hand on appointment.

But Giles and Grandma go marching on.

As this brilliant new annual proves, the humour, the compassion, and the capacity for observing human frailties, Carl Giles shows no signs whatsoever of diminishing.

He is truly a giant of our time.

V E DAY 1945: "Now it's over, I'll get some leave and repair that gutter and put a couple of boards in that fence."

V E DAY 1985

Sunday Express, May 5th, 1985

"I'm not taking you to court over who owns it, but it'll be the Old Bailey for the pair of you if I catch it near my goldfish pond again!"

Sunday Express, June 17th, 1984

"You'd be a very foolish little linesman to foot-fault the Chairman too often and still expect that promotion."

Sunday Express, June 24th, 1984

"Patience, Madam. Mrs. Remington's poodles psychological disturbance has priority over your suspected rumbling appendix."

(Headline of the day: Surgeon let vet help in operation)

Daily Express, June 28th, 1984

"I see Navratilova, Botham and Scargill still get more coverage in the Press than prize marrows."

Sunday Express, July 1st, 1984

"Grandma's practising her July 4th protest outside the U.S. base—There'll Always Be An England in the morning and God Bless America in the N.C.O.'s bar in the evening."

Daily Express, July 3rd, 1984

"Don't forget—we've been staying with Aunty Pru in Blackpool, not with the crooks on the Costa del Sol."

Daily Express, July 5th, 1984

"If your licence does go up to £10, in future the slippers will be delivered right here."

Sunday Express, July 8th, 1984

"Don't forget to tell them there's talk about banning drink at cricket matches—you'll need these."

Daily Express, July 12th, 1984

"He's stalling! That's the tenth call to check if there's any chance of the dock strike spreading to London Airport."

Sunday Express, July 15th, 1984

"I suppose they fell off the back of a banana boat onto the back of your lorry."

Daily Express, July 17th, 1984

"The dog won't go for you but SHE will—about our £116 million profits and her being later than ever."

Daily Express, July 19th, 1984

"Birdies, eagles, albatrosses—here's to the St. Andrews bird-watchers weekend."

Sunday Express, July 22nd, 1984

"Latest report on the school hols front—they've all gone out to buy Olympic javelins."

Daily Express, July 24th, 1984

"If I'd known they were going to cut down council spending this much, I wouldn't have taken the bloomin' job."

Daily Express, July 26th, 1984

"I took an overdose of pep pills for the high jump."

Sunday Express, July 29th, 1984

"She wrote to the shoe people and said she'd watch the Olympics in her bare feet for half the price, but they turned her down."

Daily Express, July 31st, 1984

"That's the 23rd ball your little Trinidad chum has knocked out to sea!"

Daily Express, August 2nd, 1984

"If he once mentions Olympic Games or tells us we're all runners in the great race against evil, I'm withdrawing to the Spotted Cow."

Sunday Express, August 5th, 1984

"We've got a complaint—they've been in Corfu for three-quarters of an hour and haven't been propositioned."

Daily Express, August 7th, 1984

"Awake, Perseus—if you can go as fast as Tessa Sanderson's javelin, you might just catch the 7.10."

Daily Express, August 9th, 1984

"Do you realise you are hindering his chances of being the first grouse served in the Ritz on the glorious 12th?"

Sunday Express, August 12th, 1984

"Very well, I'll just let you hit Michael Whitaker—then I don't want to hear any more Olympics for the next four years."

Daily Express, August 14th, 1984

"The Arts Council considers my Lady With Fan reflects the classic simplicity of the age and has granted me 200 grand."

Daily Express, August 16th, 1984

"The holiday in Spain did them good—got them in training for the start of football."

Sunday Express, August 19th, 1984

"If he wins a million we might look forward to a new washer on this tap."

Daily Express, August 21st, 1984

"First! You can forget Express stories about the changing face of seaside landladies—this one hasn't."

Daily Express, August 23rd, 1984

"Translated, he's saying he sent six of his Rolls to Rolls-Royce to have the ashtrays emptied and how do we propose to get them back with the dock strike on?"

Sunday Express, August 26th, 1984

"First job, Clarence—Mrs Jones's bunged-up drain.
Can't be worse than watching Town play their first game yesterday."

Daily Express, August 28th, 1984

"Of course Daddy will be upset to learn Boy George has changed his hairstyle—but don't tell him now."

Sunday Express, September 2nd, 1984

"I'm going to try it this term—last year Chalky was the only teacher who didn't get done up."

Daily Express, September 4th, 1984

"I can understand Joan Collins knocking five years off, but that one stuck ten years on to get her pension early."

Daily Express, September 6th, 1984

"This will put the NCVO report that Britain is a nation of Happy Families to the test—
here comes Uncle Sidney and his happy breed."

Sunday Express, September 9th, 1984

"I should forget the plastic bags, Mr Robson—the way they're playing, I don't think the photographers will bother to turn up."

(Headline of the day: Coal boss McGregor wears plastic bag to dodge cameraman)

Daily Express, September 11th, 1984

"Lady! I've been reading doctors' handwriting all me life—your prescription says '24 Teddy Bears, 1 doz. horse pills, and a box of mystique eyeshade'."

Daily Express, September 13th, 1984

"Have you any other security besides a fair chance of winning the Daily Express £1 million?"

Daily Express, September 18th, 1984

"I think what Frau Meyerburger is trying to tell you is that she had only just got her garden tidy since the Second World War."

Daily Express, September 20th, 1984

"Remember last year it was Captain Mark Phillips jumping horses over Land Rovers?"

Sunday Express, September 23rd, 1984

"Whether we can afford the new Star Wars video depends on how much we can get for him on the baby market."

(Headline of the day: Storm erupts over baby-selling)

Daily Express, September 25th, 1984

"I think calling the farmers a conniving bunch of hedge and tree slashers in your first sermon was perhaps unfortunate."

Sunday Express, September 30th, 1984

"I am aware that solicitors may advertise as from the 1st inst., now take it down!"

Daily Express, October 2nd, 1984

"That one taught me English Language that I didn't even learn in the Army."

Daily Express, October 4th, 1984

"She's half Bolshevik all the year round but let anyone criticise the Queen's hat . . ."

(Headline of the day: QUEEN'S TOUR: Canadians criticise H.M.'s dress)

Sunday Express, October 7th, 1984

"It makes a change from miners' helmets!"

(Headline of the day: Bishops criticised police in miners dispute)

Daily Express, October 11th, 1984

"Oh, Elmer! To think that it might have been one of our very own little bombs!"

Sunday Express, October 14th, 1984

"No, I do not want to come and see Mr Jones's smashing new Jaguar XJ-SC 3.6!"

Daily Express, October 16th, 1984

"Nothing wrong with his bedside manner—I only called to give him a check-up!"

Daily Express, October 18th, 1984

"We have a report that your boy is celebrating Trafalgar Day on top of Nelson's column."

Sunday Express, October 21st, 1984

"She monopolises racing and snooker on BBC and the soap operas on ITV but never puts a penny in the kitty for the licence."

Daily Express, October 25th, 1984

"You didn't pull the Royal Britannia off the mud! You putta the Queen Mamma on the mud."

Sunday Express, October 28th, 1984

"I'd have thought you might let them get Guy Fawkes night over first."

Sunday Express, November 4th, 1984

"Well I certainly knows of a better 'ole—they're serving Caviar, Swan in Aspic and Crepes Suzette in that one!"

Daily Express, November 6th, 1984

"What shall we do today—a Boy George over the shoulder or the new upswept like Princess Diana?"

Daily Express, November 8th, 1984

"We didn't have all this Cordon Bleu when I was your batman in the last lot—I used to boil your eggs in our 'ot tea."

Sunday Express, November 11th, 1984

"They've sure got Scorpio's number today—'Venus is about to move out of the financial area of your solar horoscope but before it does it will shower one further blessing on you'."

Daily Express, November 13th, 1984

"What do ya mean 'What kept me?' — 100,000 £1 coins to the ton, that's what kept me!"

Daily Express, November 15th, 1984

"If you accidentally put a pound coin in the kitty by mistake that's your bad luck, mate!"

Sunday Express, November 18th, 1984

"I can't make them out—they poison their sweets to kill their children, their children give them to us, we throw them back . . ."

Daily Express, November 20th, 1984

"Mike says to lay off phone boxes—he's a shareholder now."

Daily Express, November 22nd, 1984

"Right! Bring her in—she's jumped the gun. Sunday trading doesn't start till 1986."

Sunday Express, November 25th, 1984

"It's the Animal Liberation Front protesting about donkeys with three people up doing Jerusalem to Bethlehem without a break."

Daily Express, November 27th, 1984

"Elsie asked me to remind you, my Lord, that in the larder you promised to get her star billing in the House of Lords' TV show."

(Headline of the day: First Lords Debate televised)

Daily Express, November 29th, 1984

"Leo, I admire your determination not to let the cuts in student grants worry us—
like answering an ad. to get me a paper round."

Sunday Express, December 2nd, 1984

"Whoa there! We warned you if you went for over 100,000 Telecom shares you might end up with none!"

Daily Express, December 4th, 1984

"And what are all your uncles and aunties going to say if you send them topless herald angels singing?"

Daily Express, December 6th, 1984

"I suppose one may say there are those among us that have to work every bloody Sunday."

(Headline of the day: Sunday Shopping for Christmas)

Sunday Express, December 9th, 1984

"If we start a rumour that Prince Andrew is dating one of your girls, these glass slippers will go like Telecom shares."

Daily Express, December 11th, 1984

"In your case why wait until 35?"

Daily Express, December 13th, 1984

"That's the holly and the mistletoe—now all we want is an almighty bang when dad blows the fuses, then we know it's Christmas."

Sunday Express, December 16th, 1984

"Lady, if it's mod you're after, Miss Selfridge is in Oxford Street."

Daily Express, December 18th, 1984

"Noel! I've just won a Christmas holiday for one in the Bahamas—plane leaves tonight!"

Daily Express, December 20th, 1984

"We Three Kings of Orient are . . ."

Sunday Express, December 23rd, 1984

"Well that should put paid to the legend of Father Christmas."

Daily Express, December 24th, 1984

"I know they haven't got a sale on—that's one of my boy's Christmas presents going back the moment they open."

Daily Express, December 27th, 1984

"Vera read about all those little dogs that wanted a home after Christmas."

Sunday Express, December 30th, 1984

"Hoots everybody! Grandma and her sister are back from their Over Sixties Hogmanay party."

Daily Express, December 31st, 1984

"Could you wrap them in holly paper—I forgot to get the wife a Christmas present."

Daily Express, January 3rd, 1985

" 'Ullo, 'Ullo, what we got here?"

Sunday Express, January 6th, 1985

"One package holiday brochure for sunny Spain . . . no stamp, 34p to pay."

Daily Express, January 10th, 1985

"Well done! Only six seconds slower than his running time at the Newmarket Spring Meeting."

Sunday Express, January 13th, 1985

"I'm not taking a bloody long time to cross the road—my new mini electric has got a flat battery."

Daily Express, January 15th, 1985

"Don't ask me why—he just hit me!"

Daily Express, January 17th, 1985

"Mind you don't make them too fat to fly away from the cat!"

Sunday Express, January 20th, 1985

"It's not Black Rod, M'Lord—the lady has left her box of Persil just behind the Throne."

Daily Express, January 22nd, 1985

"Hundred on Anne to beat Piggott—I haven't the heart to tell him they ain't in the same race."

Daily Express, January 24th, 1985

"She's not kerb-crawling in your sense of the word, Sir, she uses the kerb to find her way home."

Sunday Express, January 27th, 1985

"In that case what's the point in having talks?"

Daily Express, January 29th, 1985

"Another one discovered gold in his garden to get us to dig it over?"

Sunday Express, February 3rd, 1985

"You've got to give them ten out of ten for guts—calling Chalkie a scab!"

Daily Express, February 7th, 1985

"Butch would have won—but I think he dropped a few points when he took the sleeve out of the judge's jacket."

Sunday Express, February 10th, 1985

"On the other hand, if you don't let me through with my sheep you aren't going to get very far either."

Daily Express, February 12th, 1985

"Forty quids' worth of roses because HE thinks SHE sent him a Valentine's card . . . actually, I sent it."

Daily Express, February 14th, 1985

"If I'd seen your father nude I doubt if there'd be half a dozen of you running around now."

Daily Express, February 21st, 1985

"He's tapping your phone—says he's dropped his detector and would you call the Fire Brigade to help get him down."

Sunday Express, February 24th, 1985

"Mine's caught on quick . . . 'you pay' he says."

Daily Express, February 26th, 1985

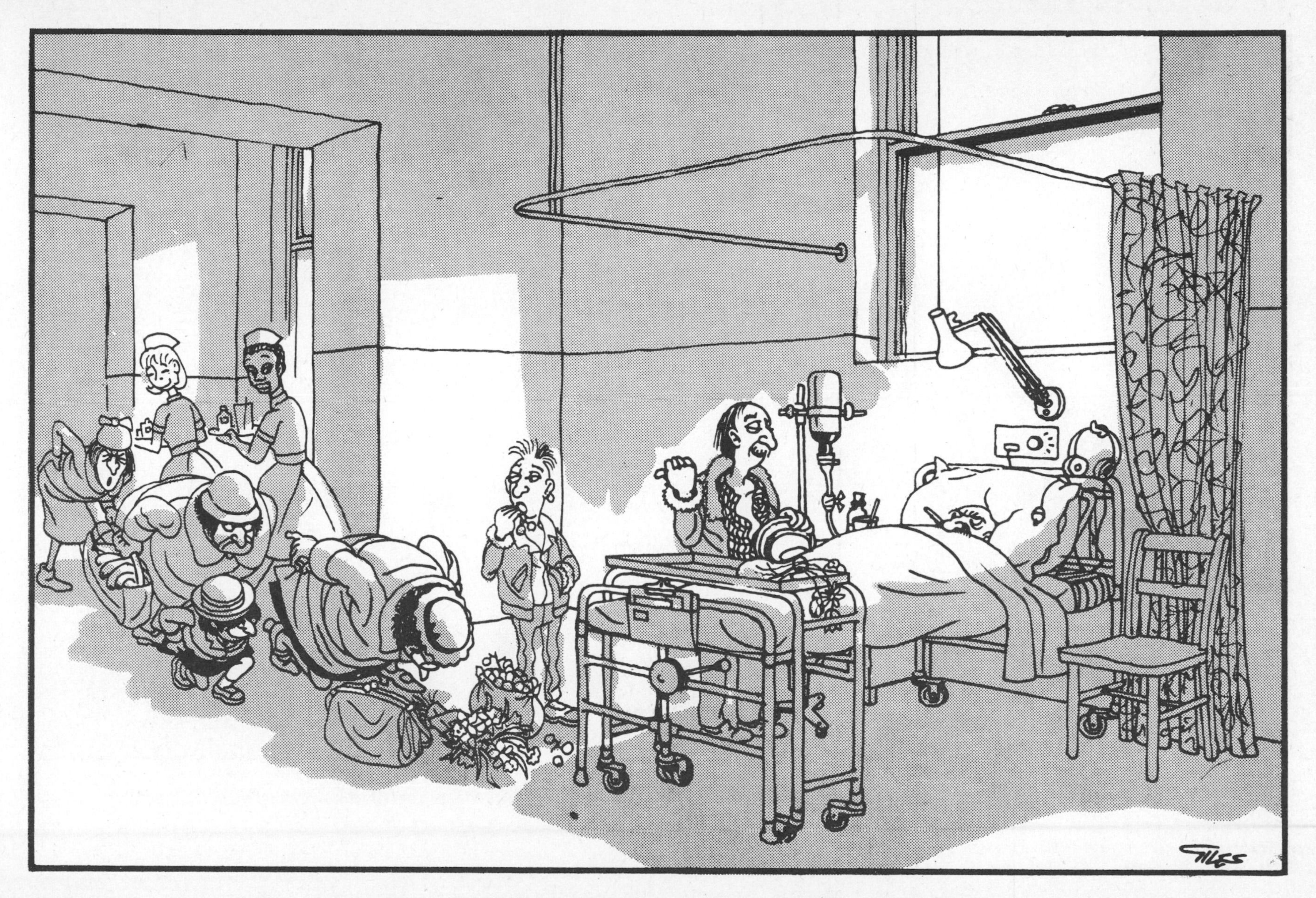

"The curtsey is in case you got a drop of Prince Charles's blood in yer."

(Headline of the day: Prince Charles Becomes Blood Donor)

Sunday Express, March 3rd, 1985

"Know what I miss? The gentle thud of lumps of coal on my helmet and the restful calls of the pickets."

Daily Express, March 5th, 1985

"I reckon Grandma drank the Thames and Clyde put together before TV was invented."

Sunday Express, March 10th, 1985

"She wants them all cut up for examination—who wrote that article about the public not getting enough meat in their bangers?"

Daily Express, March 12th, 1985

"Your wife's Irish eyes aren't smiling, Paddy—I think she's just heard we found 2 Grand in your boots."

Daily Express, March 14th, 1985

"Oh Lord! I forgot—it's Mother's Day."

Sunday Express, March 17th, 1985

"Here is a recording made on Budget Day 1957: 'If they put any more on cigarettes, I'm definitely giving them up'."

Daily Express, March 19th, 1985

"She's backing you to win in the first race of the Flat and says she'll be right behind you."

Daily Express, March 21st, 1985

"You're wasting your time—the Princess didn't actually tell Wogan she was *looking* for a job as a lorry driver."

(Headline of the day: Princess Anne on Chat Show "If things came to the worse I could always drive a lorry".)

Sunday Express, March 24th, 1985

"Oh, I don't know—for the last six Nationals, he's finished the course without me."

Daily Express, March 28th, 1985

"Don't take it out on us all the way back South—it was you who said you read they were holding the Grand National in Glasgow this year."

Sunday Express, March 31st, 1985

"Make up your minds before the Tate Gallery snaps them up for £1m—
one gnome with his head off and a bunch of bananas."

(Headline of the day: Tate pays £1 million for surrealist painting)

Daily Express, April 4th, 1985

"Next—'Make hole to take two inch waste-pipe'."

Sunday Express, April 7th, 1985

"Well, that's our horror stories for Easter—now I'll get in and listen to Bugs Bunny tell me his."

Daily Express, April 9th, 1985

"She's won me moneybox, piggy bank, half an Easter egg, me conkers and me knife—I reckon she's on dope!"

Daily Express, April 11th, 1985

"No, we haven't got a tramp moved in at the bottom of the garden, like Tony Benn—that's dad."

Sunday Express, April 14th, 1985

"Given the choice of jet-lag from doing seven countries in 11 days
and my three home from school for two weeks I know which I'd choose."

(Headline of the day: Mrs. Thatcher home after marathon Asian tour.)

Daily Express, April 16th, 1985

"She's wearing a flowing azure chiffon dress with batwing sleeves and a beautiful pea-green hat."

Sunday Express, April 21st, 1985

"Your electric fence didn't stop them coming to tea—they've all bought little rubber boots."

Sunday Express, April 28th, 1985

"I remember letting her have extra food rations for the Victory Street Party in 1945—
and we all know where they finished up."

Daily Express, May 7th, 1985

"She didn't recognise you in your new uniform—she thought you were food."

Sunday Express, May 12th, 1985

"The new anti kerb-crawling Bill does not apply to us, Sir."

Sunday Express, May 19th, 1985

"They don't make them like they used to, mate."

Daily Express, May 28th, 1985

"Of course Mummy hasn't stopped loving you because she said she'd hang anyone who reduced school leaving age to 14."

Daily Express, May 30th, 1985

"I wasn't complaining about us being late getting it in the water—
I simply said the nights start drawing in again this month."

Sunday Express, June 2nd, 1985

"Morning Murph, have a good night? By the way—where's the horse?"

Daily Express, June 4th, 1985

"Mrs Thatcher would certainly give Grandma's State Benefits a radical overhaul
if she knew they all went on Lester Piggott yesterday."

Daily Express, June 6th, 1985

"On the other hand I think it's *you* who's wearing the funny clothes for June."

Sunday Express, June 9th, 1985

"There you are! You didn't think we would let you spend Father's Day on your own."

Sunday Express, June 16th, 1985

"Two, Royal Enclosure, Ascot, please."

Daily Express, June 18th, 1985